GW00673281

EVIDENCES
OF THE FLOOD

by

W. W. GREENMAN

———————

Published by the
GOSPEL STANDARD STRICT BAPTIST TRUST LTD
1977

8 Roundwood Gardens, Harpenden, Herts AL5 3AJ
England

0 903556 50 2

*Printed in Great Britain
at the University Press, Oxford
by Vivian Ridler
Printer to the University*

CONTENTS

PREFACE

When we first invited Mr. W. Greenman to contribute to The Friendly Companion we did so with the hope that his extensive study of this subject would be of help to our young people who are faced with the God dishonouring teaching of Evolution at school. This objective, we are thankful to say, has, we believe, in some measure, been attained. Knowing however that the evil tenets have so deeply wormed their way into all sections of reading matter, and that one generation is always rapidly following another, and is likely to be contaminated if we take not heed, the Gospel Standard Strict and Particular Baptist Trust Ltd., felt it desirable to finance this reprint for use in a much larger circle than their own.

And now, as we briefly review the lengths to which man has gone to deny the Divine Creation, and the Flood of Divine judgment, and bear in mind the prophecy made by the apostle Peter, we cannot but be thankful that the Lord has raised up so many able men to maintain His cause. No such defenders of the truth will be required however to confirm the second part of the same prophecy, namely, that "the heavens shall pass away with a great noise, and the elements shall melt with fervent heat, and the earth also and the works therein shall be burned up." 2 Peter 3, 10.

L. R. Broome,

Editor, "Friendly Companion",—1972

1.

EVIDENCES OF THE FLOOD

Chapters 6, 7 and 8 of The Book of Genesis record one of the most important, impressive and solemn events in the history of the world, namely The Flood. With the exception of eight human beings the whole of mankind was overtaken and destroyed in this judgment. The reason was the anger of God against man's wickedness, violence and corruption. Genesis 6:5.

Now, as the Flood covered all the earth, we might well expect to find marks and evidences of it in many parts of the earth, scattered over all the continents. This is exactly what we do find, but since these marks are so seldom known, it is the purpose of this booklet to mention several of them, so that if our young people should perhaps be told that we no longer believe in the Flood, they may not be soon shaken in mind, since they can point to the evidence of it in all lands.

We should expect, since all nations descended from Noah's three sons, that almost all of the older nations would have some account of the Flood in their histories or traditions which had been passed down to them by word of mouth or in writing from their forefathers. These accounts would of course become less detailed and accurate as the centuries went by. As a matter of fact we do find in almost all the oldest nations on earth, accounts of a world-wide flood, sent for the wickedness of mankind to destroy all flesh from off the earth, except one man and his family who were saved in an ark, together with two animals of every kind. These accounts, numbering about 100, are found in the writings and traditions of Babylon, Nineveh, China, Greece, Egypt,

1

India, Mexico, Australia, N. & S. America, the Polynesians, the Red Indians, the Fijians and many others; that is, from all continents. We have the account from Nineveh in the British Museum, from 2,500 years ago, and even that was copied from an earlier account, of a date much nearer to the time of the Flood itself. The dates of the kings of Babylonia were in early days recorded as having been so many years before the Flood or so many years after it. All these early writings from such widely spread nations can only mean that the Flood was a real event, an undoubted historical fact of great importance, since all the nations had sprung from the one family of Noah. Even to this day, we speak in general terms of the western nations as Japhetic nations (after Japheth), the eastern nations as Semitic (after Shem), and the African nations as Hamitic (after Ham), the three sons of Noah. These groups after thousands of years, have many subdivisions.

These evidences, together with many geological, geographical and other scientific facts, which appear in the following pages, show that in every continent there are signs of a world-wide flood, and such signs as can be understood in no other way.

2

ANIMAL REMAINS

Our next step is to show the existence of countless animal remains, buried in sedimentary or water-laid deposits all over the earth. These fossils are usually bones found in caves on high land, and covered with a layer of sand or gravel washed in by the waters as they reached the height of the caves; or, secondly, they are found as huge stretches of bones of various types of animals often mingled together and buried quite often under layers of sediment of varying thicknesses, some surprisingly thick. All this could have happened in only one way. Tidal waves, in the first days of the Flood, caused by the breaking through of "the fountains of the great deep," Gen. 7:11, swept across the land, drowning, and carrying with them, the animals in their path, with also vast quantities of mud, sand, gravel, clay and chalk. After travelling long distances the speed of the water became small enough for the dead animals and silt to fall to the bottom, where the sediment hardened, encasing the animals in sedimentary rock. Amongst these animals of various kinds were huge multitudes of fish already in the waters before they swept over the land, and as these fish were choked by the mud in the waters, and buried under it, shoals of fossil fish are found in many countries. It is a startling fact that shoals of fossil fish have been found near the tops of the Alps, and on mountain tops in many other parts of the world, as well as on flatter parts of the earth. Truly the waters covered the mountains. Of course, if the waters were above the mountains in some countries, they were just as high in all countries.

In addition to this, millions of skeletons of animals have been found on lower land. Dr. Broome, the South African fossilologist, estimated that the Karroo district of 200,000 sq. miles contained thousands of millions of skeletons of animals buried. In all continents there are large dinosaur 'cemeteries' containing hundreds of skeletons of these animals which had been washed into valleys and buried in the mud. In the Paluxy River Bed, in Texas, there are fossilised footprints of dinosaurs mingled with those of men. So the dinosaurs, instead of living 60 million years ago as some so-called 'scientists' pretend, were living, with men, just before the Flood. The human footprints were 15 inches long, which agrees with Genesis 6:4, ' There were giants in the earth in those days."

Another outstanding fact is the existence in all continents of caves almost always on high ground, literally crammed with the skeletons of a strange mixture of animals which had climbed the mountain sides to avoid the rising flood water, and had all crowded together in the caves, seeking to escape, but as the water still rose it entered the caves, drowned the animals, and left a covering of gravel on many of them. These caves are found in France, Cyprus, Malta, Sicily, California,

Maryland, Java, Australia, S. America, and Yorkshire in England. The Victoria Cave in Yorkshire, at an altitude of 1,450 feet contained the bones of the grizzly bear, bison, fox, reindeer, mammoth, hare, hyaena and hippopotamus, when excavated in 1870. The Elbolton cave 800 feet up, excavated in 1888 contained bears, reindeer and mammoths. The Raygill Quarries at 750 feet, excavated in 1880, contained bones of bears, hyaenas, elephant, lion, hippopotamus and slender-nosed rhinoceros. It is clear that nothing but a flood would have driven such strange mixtures of animals into caves in all parts of the earth and buried them together.

One more astonishing fact is the existence of a salt-water sea in a fold of the Andes Mountains in Bolivia in S. America, at an altitude of 12,500 feet. There are no salt-bearing rocks or streams in those parts, so the only way in which this salt-sea could have been deposited is for it to have been left there when the waters covered the earth, and as the Flood subsided it remained trapped in the mountains. At first it was some 400 miles long and 100 miles wide, but has slowly evaporated to much smaller proportions since.

This mountain-locked sea, the shoals of fish on mountain tops, the remains of drowned animals on high ground, the huge shoals of fish on lower land, and bone deposits in all continents all prove beyond a doubt that the whole earth was flooded in every part.

It is noteworthy that in no place on earth do the fossils show the least sign of evolution from one species to another. All the fossils appear in completely distinct species, with not a single connecting link between any of them.

3

PROOFS IN THE ROCKS

We come next to those geological and geographical evidences which are before our eyes. These evidences deal with the rocks of the earth, and the state of the land. The most complex evidences will be avoided in this booklet, as it is hoped to keep it understandable to the younger readers, as well as informative to the older ones.

There are two main kinds of rock on the earth, the igneous or volcanic, of which many of our mountains and plateaux consist, and secondly, sedimentary rocks of many sorts, namely those which have been swilled into position in the form of gravel, sand, clay and chalk, etc., and have, under the tremendous pressure of the flood waters, and the weight of still further deposits of sediment, become compressed and hardened into solid masses. These layers of sediment, as already noticed, were loaded with multitudes of various kinds of animals or their bones, which became encased in the rocks as they hardened. These are called fossils (which means 'dug up'). They must have formed very quickly, or they would not have formed at all, as the bodies would have decayed or disappeared. It is very important to notice that fossils are only found in waterlaid rocks. Now, although so-called 'science' books give the impression that the fossils in the lowest rocks are small, and of simple form, slowly changing, as we come up through the rocks, into larger and more complex forms, till at last we come to the highest rocks and find the biggest and most complex animals, and some human fossils, this is simply not true. This does not occur in a single place on earth. If it were true, and if the simple forms had slowly evolved into slightly more complex ones, there would have been countless millions of animals slightly different from those below and above them, but no distinct species at all. The exact opposite is true. All the fossils appear in distinct and separate species, quite different from other species near them, with no connecting links between any of the species. If mutations or sudden changes are suggested as a method of evolution, it is well to know that these are always within the species, never from one species to another.

Also in no place on earth do we find more than a very few species in layers near each other, mostly two or three, instead of the hundreds of species which children are allowed to imagine to be there. The next fact is almost unknown, namely that the species that are there are by no means always ascending from the simple to the complex, but in very numerous cases the complex forms are lowest, and the simple forms above them. Neither is there a single connecting link between any of the species anywhere. If evolution were true there should have been millions of links; and could anyone at all intelligent believe that any particular species stayed at one single spot on earth for millions of years, so that their bodies might build up a stratum or layer of fossilised remains at a rate of less than a thousandth of an inch per century? This is what evolutionists would have us believe, from their ridiculous datings of strata. And anyhow, the fossils are not in well-ordered series, but in hundreds of cases in topsy-turvy arrangement. This again disagrees with evolution.

We read in Genesis 7: 11 and 12, ". . . the same day were all the fountains of the great deep broken up, and the windows of heaven were opened, and the rain was on the earth forty days and forty nights," and here the word "all" is important. This means that the sea-bed in very many places all round the earth became greatly disturbed by volcanic action throwing out such stupendous amounts of water (and probably lava, since the fountains are not called specifically water fountains) that the seas overflowed the land and added their waters in vast quantities to the downpour from the skies for 40 days. Since the seas are approximately seven-tenths of the earth's surface and the land only three-tenths, while the average depth of the sea is 13,000 feet, and the average height of the land above sea level only 2,500 feet, it is evident what a tremendous effect the filling of the seas, and the raising of the sea-bed from volcanic action would have. Vast quantities of water would be hurled about, carrying huge amounts of silt of various kinds across the flooded world. These would be deposited in various orders, with the species they happened to be carrying, in almost all parts of the earth. This is exactly what we do find. Some people say that a tidal wave travelling across the surface of the oceans would have capsized the Ark. This again is not true. In recent times, at Krakatoa, 1883, at Chile, 1960, and at Alaska since then, tidal waves have been thrown one-third of the way round the world at speeds of 450/500 miles an hour and yet they were only a few inches high on the open sea, but when they reached land they piled up to heights of 40 to 100 feet. Out at sea however they would not have capsized a rowing boat. The 100 foot wave from Krakatoa was only 9 inches high as it passed Aden.

One more tremendously outstanding fact is the following. Three quarters of the land of the earth is covered with sedimentary rock, which speaks volumes, and only one quarter is volcanic. Since this water-laid material, quite often loaded with fossils is found in all parts of the earth, and, as already noticed, even on the mountain tops of almost all the big ranges, it proves beyond dispute that the whole earth was flooded.

Coal-beds too can only be accounted for intelligently by reference to the Flood. Recent coal geologists have agreed that the many seams of coal lying one above the other, with layers of earth between the seams can only be rationally explained in the following way. When tidal waves swept over the land, they would unroot trees and carry them with other materials until conditions arrested this, and they were deposited, with almost immediately a layer of earthy sediment to cover them. Several more waves would bring further layers of trees, and further deposits of thousands of tons of sliding sediment to bury them, thus giving the well-known 'seams'. Now a remarkable occurrence in 1882 at Alt-Breisach near Freiburg was noticed by Petzoldt during the building of a bridge. When huge blocks of stone were slid into position over wooden beams, the wood very quickly became blackened, at the centre of the beams resembling anthracite, and nearer the surface resembling house coal. The change was brought about by friction and pressure. This is exactly what thousands of tons of sliding rock-material during the Flood

7

would do to the trunks underneath. Furthermore, when a solitary tree trunk also turned to coal is found standing up through several seams of coal, it is only logical to conclude that it became wedged in that position and remained there while the other seams were deposited round it in a matter of hours or days. There appears to be no other feasible explanation.

Thus, once more, the evidence when carefully examined fits in perfectly with the account of the Flood, in Genesis.

4

HUMAN REMAINS AND FRAUDULENT EVIDENCE

An earlier passage contained a number of references to fossils of animals. It did not however contain any reference to human fossils, but since large numbers of these have been found as well, it is necessary to mention them. The following facts are tremendously important. Nearly all the books we meet are strangely silent about the large numbers of fossils of human beings which have been found and which resemble 'modern man', showing that men of 'fossil ages' were exactly as they are today. Many of the books however contain chapter after chapter of stories of supposed ancestors of man, but fail to mention that no ape-man has ever been found. They show drawings of supposed ape-men, generally with a bent posture, receding forehead, receding chin, but protruding upper jaw, with also a very small cranium. No such creature has ever been found. Whole strings of such drawings are shown on charts, or in many library and school text-books, pretending to show that ape-men gradually changed to human beings. This is not true. The fossils which have been found and named ape-men fossils are mostly tiny fragments of bone, often too small for anyone to be sure whether they belonged to a man or some sort of animal. A fossil knee-cap of an elephant was claimed for some years to be part of the skull of an ape-man. A single tooth of an extinct peccary (a kind of pig) was imagined to be neither truly human, nor truly apelike, hence was said to be half-human, half-apelike, so was imagined to have belonged to an ape-man who was called

8

Hesperopithecus, and drawn in books and newspapers as a missing link. The fact that the remainder of the skeleton of the peccary was later found, was kept very quiet.

The Piltdown skull which for forty years was considered by many as the most important discovery ever made, was proved not long ago to be a fraud. Most of the skull anyway was made of plaster of Paris, with a small bit of human cranium a few inches long on top, and the jaw of a chimpanzee attached below. The teeth had been filed off to the lengths of human teeth but incorrectly shaped, and the jaw had been stained with Potassium Diochromate to make it look as old as the bit of cranium. This co-called ape-man was said to be 500,000 years old, but the scientist who recently analysed it, said the scrap of cranium was from a woman of only 500 years ago, and the jaw was from a recent chimpanzee. This shows at a glance the utter falsity and worthlessness of so-called 'datings' of fossils.

The Java 'ape-man' was for thirty years thought to be also extremely important as it consisted of a human thigh-bone, and a bit of apelike cranium. However, its discoverer admitted after 30 years that he had found true human skulls with the human thigh bone. The skull which had been used instead of these was found at a distance and has been stated to be that of a large gibbon. Other 'ape-men' have been imagined from a horse's tooth, the bone of a bear's hind leg, and the skeleton of a pet monkey.

There have been found, however, very many remains of true human beings, similar to us today. Some of these have been very incorrectly drawn, making them look rather ape-like. This has been grossly done about Neanderthal man, a European race closely resembling many people today and recognised as truly human. Very few books mention Cro-Magnon man found in considerable numbers in Europe, but possessing a large, fine stature, with an equally fine head with a splendid cranium, far better than most people's today. In various places the deeper deposits have yielded splendid skeletons of gigantic human beings, far larger than the Cro-Magnon man. Truly "There were giants in the earth in those days", Gen: 6:4. Peking man was similar to the Neanderthal and used huge fires for lime burning. Some of the fires have left heaps of ashes 100 yards long, 30 yards wide and 7 yards high. Calaveras and Castenodola skeletons were just like ours, and have been found in large numbers. Thus modern types of man have been found in earlier or deeper deposits than the scraps of bone which have been falsely called ape-men, and so these modern-type men could not have descended from the 'ape-men' which were supposed to have been their ancestors. Many scientists now agree.

Scarcely anyone has heard of footprints made by a man wearing sandals, in trilobite beds in the 'Cambrian' rock in Utah, U.S.A., discovered in 1968. These footprints had trilobites (extinct tiny crab-like creatures) actually inside them, strongly suggesting that the human being trod on the trilobites while the rock was still soft. This makes the Cambrian rock as recent as the other rocks.

It is encouraging to find that some of the newer school books on biology make scarcely any reference at all to Evolution which was very widely accepted as recently as only ten years ago. Many new books refute it, very clearly.

One of the worst frauds was in connection with 'Peking Man', so called, or Sinanthropus. Real men found at Peking, were much as we are today. But the creatures which were until recently, and in some books still are, called 'Peking Man' were found in the ashes of one of the huge lime-burning fires mixed with the bones of other animals which had been killed and eaten by real men. After several years of attempts to state these remains to be semi-human, they were shown to be nothing more than the skulls of baboons and large monkeys whose heads had all been pierced in order to extract the brains which were a great delicacy. Several plaster casts of some of these skulls were made very inaccurately, then the skulls (about 30 of them) were all destroyed. These skulls having been found in the ashes of fires made for lime-burning for house-building must have been deposited there by civilized human beings who lived in and made houses, and so the skulls which had been claimed as semi-human and about 500,000 years old, proved to be quite modern monkey's skulls. Some similarity with human beings was at first suggested for the apes of Africa, called Australopithecines. These are no longer considered to be connected with humans. True Peking men are now dated at well after the Flood date. So, we see that in early days, as shown by genuine human fossils which have been found in great numbers, men were often just as they are today, but some of the earliest were far bigger, finer and more intelligent than the men of today. Also, where we find early remains of man, we find in many cases that a form of civilization existed, in some respects far in advance of ours today. For instance, at Ur of the Chaldees where Abram lived at first, the children in the schools were taught an arithmetical method of working out cube-roots, which would be beyond the grasp of many adults today. The houses were well-built, with plastered walls. Also in the pyramids of Egypt, the mummified bodies are wrapped in fine linen, containing twice as many threads to the inch as our finest linen today. We read too of Egyptian barbers shaving their customers; and a razor 3,000 years old, taken from a pyramid recently, was still sharp enough to shave a person. Being an alloy it had not rusted, this also showing a civilized knowledge of smelting.

But to continue with fossils. We should expect in a worldwide flood that the smaller and denser animals such as shell-fish would be some of the first to be buried. Those that could move away, such as vertebrate fish would be buried later. Later still, vertebrate land animals would be overcome, and lastly the larger, stronger animals, and man having climbed to higher ground, would be drowned and buried. In many cases this is so, but as mentioned earlier, in many cases the very opposite is true, where different tidal waves swept perhaps pterodactyls into position followed by shell-fish, and so on. Now since this is flatly contrary to the idea of evolution, the evolutionists have invented what they call 'thrusts', by which they pretend that the soil containing the shell-fish is still older than the soil below, but has been pushed in some cases thousands of miles from another part of the globe, without leaving any traces or signs of such a tremendous happening, till it came to rest on the 'younger' stratum beneath. In one case they pretend that a tremendous layer of 'older' rock in the Mythen Peak in the Alps was pushed all the way from Africa to Switzerland, without leaving any trace of such a stupendous movement. All this nonsense is talked because evolutionists pretend that the fossils in these upper strata were on the earth before the fossils in the lower strata. Again this is imagined because they think that only one type of animal lived on the earth at any one time. This very basic idea of the evolutionists is flatly contradicted where we get a layer of fossils of a wide variety of types all buried together, again, all of distinct species, without any links between them. The Flood explains it beautifully, just as it explains Cretaceous and Jurassic layers lying on top of or beneath a Triassic stratum. These names of layers with the 'dates' assigned to them really signify nothing. The sediments were laid in the order we find them, by the Flood.

All this incredible nonsense was invented to uphold the so called 'scientific' theory of Uniformity, which says that the things which we see going on around us in the universe are the same things as have always been going on without variation throughout the past. Peter, in his second epistle, chapter 3, verse 4, says the language of scoffers in the last days will be "Where is the promise of his coming? for since the fathers fell asleep, all things continue as they were from the beginning of the creation," and in verses 5 and 6. "For this they willingly are ignorant of, that by the word of God the heavens were of old, and the earth standing out of the water and in the water: Whereby the world that then was, being overflowed with water, perished."

So the scoffers of today willingly disregard the Flood, because it speaks of God's judgment on the early world, just as the same word of God, in verse 7, speaks of the final judgment.

5

'DATES' AND 'AGES'

By saying there was no Flood the so-called 'scientists' left the way open for inventing the ridiculous dates which they attached to rocks all over the earth. However, since they had no reliable way of finding out the age of a rock they decided to 'date' the rocks according to the types of fossils found in them, pretending of course that simple animals came before complex ones, etc., which has already been shown to be false. Secondly since all animals were created at the same time, i.e. within six days of each other, their fossils in the rocks could not possibly be of any use in dating them. Anyhow the dates are known to be utterly false. The deep-sea mollusc was said to have died out 280 million years ago, but some have recently been fished up alive in the Acapulco Trench off Central America. The Tua-tara was supposed to have died out 135 million years ago but has recently been found alive in New Zealand. Many other similar cases could be quoted, including that of the coelacanth caught in 1939. Could anything be more useless and misleading than to pretend to date rocks from their fossils? And as we saw previously, many of the supposed 'earlier' fossils appear in strata higher than the 'later' ones. Hence the invention of the 'thrust' theory. Instead of all this self-contradictory theory, how clearly and logically it is explained by the fact that all these rocks which are water-laid, were washed into place by the Flood.

Another thing which tends to impress the student is the calm way in which the 'scientist' speaks of ice-ages of the past, as if there was some proof of this. Some speak of four ice-ages, others of three, and some think only one has occurred. Without going into all the so-called evidence of ice-ages, the evidence must be very faulty or doubtful, if we do not know whether it is supposed to show four ice-ages or only one. Also it must be completely misread or it would give the same ideas to all. Furthermore, the famous geologist, Sir Henry Howorth stated that the marks which are supposed to be evidence of ice are more rationally understood if taken as evidences of flood water. As he did not uphold the Bible he was not trying to make the evidence support the Genesis account. He, however, did think the marks were signs of a flood, and not of ice.

Perhaps the most misleading thing about the word 'ages' is the way it is used to denote periods of time when a much better word and meaning would be 'districts'. For instance the only distinct proofs we know of an ice-age, exist at the poles today. 'Ice-districts' would be a much more accurate term. In the polar areas, hundreds of miles of land are under ice, some of it thousands of feet thick. Thus the ice-age is on now, in those districts. The stone-age was not a period of time when all the people of the earth used stone tools and weapons, hundreds of thousands of years ago, but the 'stone-age' is on now in some of the South Sea Islands, and in Central Australia where the people have nothing to use but stone and wooden tools. Cave-men did not live several thousands of years ago in all parts of the earth, where for the most part there were no caves anyway, but some men have lived in caves and some still do where caves exist here and there. These 'cave-men' are ordinary people living where caves are conveniently situated for them. Some even make their own caves by hollowing them out. In some countries today the iron-age is on, in some the atomic-age is on, and in others the space-age. Thus the supposed datings of the stone-age, iron-age and bronze-age etc. are false and misleading. Another fact seldom realised is this, that if people had been on the earth 500,000 years as pretended by evolutionists (instead of the nearly 6,000 years of the Bible) the whole earth would have been so over-populated that there would not have been standing room on the earth for a hundredth of them. The same is also true of the animals. It has been calculated that at the usual rate of doubling of population the eight persons in the ark would have produced the present world population if the Flood was about 4,500 years ago which of course it was.

This date of the Flood is approximately supported by the fact that many inland salt-water lakes existed in early historical times, but have completely dried up now. Prof. Fessenden mentions geological evidence that a sea once reached from the Caucasus to Mongolia, about 1,850 miles, and says that as late as 300 B.C. the Caspian and Aral seas were joined. Marco Polo found numerous lakes across Asia in 1280 A.D. but a few years ago Citroen travelled the same route and found none. The Flood that had filled those lakes could only have left them full enough to have lasted to these dates if the Flood itself had not been very long ago, or else the lakes would have dried out long before. Thus geological facts and history agree with the Bible account in a very convincing manner.

We have just pointed out that 'scientists' have stated that various animals not only were supposed to have lived, but also to have become extinct hundreds of millions of years ago, but they have been proved utterly wrong by the fact that those very creatures have been found alive today. If their 'datings' of animals were so utterly false and they date the rocks from the animals in them, the 'ages' they assign to the rocks are equally useless. The 'radio-carbon', and other 'radio active' methods of dating things are of necessity built upon a number of assumptions and are therefore unreliable. Lava thrown out in 1801 has been "dated" by the Potassium-Argon method as between 160 million and 3,000 million years old!! Actually it is 170 years old. Anyhow, out of hundreds of tests made on the ages of rocks only about a dozen are accepted, and very divergent results have been obtained from samples taken in the same locality. These results are therefore as unreliable as the others. The geological theory of 'uniformity' which pretends that things have always been taking place in the past as they are today, without interruption or catastrophe, is also shown to be false by the vast sediments which have been washed into position, even to the mountain tops, in the past, but are nowhere being laid today. Thus the two main arguments for vast 'ages' of rocks and fossils are false. The point of all this is that all man's pretended dating of things not seen by man and recorded as history can only be based on assumption and guesswork. The only reliable source of knowledge of pre-historic happenings is the Bible. No other knowledge is possible.

If our young readers realise this, they will not be disturbed by such guesses at the moon's 'age' as 3.5 billion years, although one piece of rock on it as big as an orange was 'dated' at 4.5 billion years. Could anything be more ridiculous and impossible to imagine? One thing does appear certain however, that the moon was never formed from part of the earth, as has been suggested in schools for many years. "He taketh the wise in their own craftiness", Job. 5, 13.

Here again the only true guide as to the origin of the earth, moon, sun and stars, as well as to the early happenings on the earth is the Bible. This gives an accurate account which fits in with all the verified geological, geographical and scientific facts observable.

Now there is no scientific reason at all for thinking that the strata were laid in any other way or at any other time than by the Flood, and in fact science agrees that all the strata we are considering are sedimentary or water-laid. Common sense observation also agrees. Moreover, as already noticed, all the varying orders of the strata with their topsy-turvyness fit in exactly with the kind of currents we should expect with a world-wide flood. There is no doubt at all that these vast sediments were water-laid. But being so vast they required a world-wide flood to lay them, and in any case they are found all over the world. Also a world-wide flood would certainly be capable of laying them. Even the tiny floods we know today are far more powerful than is often realised. An account of flood streams in the Assam area says that although the water had only risen thirteen feet, huge pieces of rock measuring some feet across were rolled along with an awful crashing, almost as easily as pebbles in an ordinary stream. An account from Utah says a flood there left a deposit several feet thick containing boulders up to 20 tons in weight. Others weighing 200 tons were washed down a slight slope. But the Flood was not merely river water but far more awful than this, flooded seas. In Scotland around 1880, a concrete block weighing 2,600 tons at the end of a breakwater was removed bodily and thrown into the water nearby, and this was just an ordinary storm at sea.

The Flood lasted over all the earth for 5 months, was many thousands of feet deep covering all the mountains, and was thrown about by submarine earthquakes which would have made the deposits as a natural consequence. Also the Flood took another 4 months to recede enough for the tops of the mountains to be seen. After another 3 months and 10 days the ground was dry.

Science is the observation and study of things as they are happening now, but science cannot possibly be the observation of things being created at the beginning.

We have seen how totally false were the 'datings' of fossils and rocks. The 'dating' of the age of oceans is even more strange. One method is based on the quantity of salt in the sea. Now salt is composed of Sodium and Chlorine united together. When the 'dating' is based on the Sodium content it comes to 50 million years, while if based on the Chlorine part of the salt it comes to 90 million years. This is unbelievably ridiculous and puts the 'dating' method to shame, and its results are utterly useless and impossible.

When we come to 'historical' dating, we have often read of the discovery of the ruins of some ancient city or village and calmly been told that the pottery shows it to have been perhaps 8,000 years old and sometimes much more. Further investigations have shown however that the 'ages' were totally wrong and they have been reduced to 5,000 years, and again to 3,000 years. This has been done in Egypt, and Babylon, and many other places. It is now known that the earliest verifiable dates from secular history were around 2,500 B.C. which is not long after the Flood. If man had been on the earth hundreds of thousands of years as evolutionists pretend, surely his history would have been recorded long ages before this date.

Older readers may have wondered how far to believe the claims of astronomers that they can measure the distances of the furthest stars and galaxies, and of course from this to estimate the age of the Universe. This is impossible in the extreme. The assumptions and sheer guess-work which are allowed in this 'estimating' shake the imagination. Dr. T. Jacobsen of the University of Washington tells us that the 'measurements' of the universe are based upon "A pure guess that the present radius of curvature is about 100 times the original Einstein radius." If this does not show how utterly false is the claim to be able to measure the distances of the stars, what does? However it is pleasant to find two scientists, Moon and Spencer, in "Binary stars and the velocity of light," saying that if their view is correct that the speed of light is not relative to the observer as Einstein thought, but constant, then the light from the furthest stars would reach the earth in 15 years. Anyhow the millions of light years calculation is based upon a 'pure guess', and is impossible to obtain in any factual way whatsoever. It is disastrous that these facts are so rarely made known that diligent search is needed to find them. Jacobsen adds, "The result is that we know nothing certain about the age of the universe." (Review of Space, Time and Creation).

Another very striking discovery has been made recently when scientists discovered a group of bristlecone pines growing in the White Mountains of California and by counting the rings in 17 of them, found the ages of the trees to be around 4,000 years. Many more of these trees are still growing. A similar discovery of giant sequoias showed that their ages were also similar. It is very confirming to find that the ages of these extremely ancient trees reach back nearly to the date of the Flood, but we have found none going back beyond this date. Thus the most reliable dates of man, and even the ages of the oldest trees agree closely with the dates in the Bible.

6

CREATION — ALMIGHTY POWER

It is very clear from what we have seen that the evidence of fossils, proves beyond doubt that the whole earth was entirely flooded.

Many people would, however, like to forget God. But we cannot forget God in anything, for "In him we live, and move, and have our being" and all things come from Him. Creation shows Him everywhere. Creation shows the existence of unthinkable energy, exquisite order in everything whether tremendously great or unimaginably small, and meticulous timing. But energy must be produced, order requires a controlling mind, and accurate timing requires a perfectly controlled flow of energy. To pretend that things could just come without a Creator is unintelligent atheism. To pretend that chaos could produce order is as ridiculous as thinking that a cement mixer if filled with millions of letters of the alphabet could churn out an encyclopaedia. To pretend that everything in nature with its existence, its order, and its beautiful timing could just happen by chance is less intelligent than thinking that a lorry-load of cricket balls if overturned in a huge field would just sort themselves out into the most beautiful patterns, and start orbiting within these patterns and keep it up continuously without colliding, and without any force to start them or keep them moving. It requires an Almighty Power with an infinitely wise mind to create a universe, place all the stars in their courses, and keep them moving in perfect timing from creation till now. We see this Power working in placing the earth at such a distance from the sun that animal and plant life can exist upon it, while the size of the earth is just right to exert the correct gravity on the atmosphere to keep the exact amount of it at the right density to suit animal and plant life, on the earth. Again the speed of the earth in travelling round the sun is just right to keep it at its correct distance from the sun in spite of the gravitational pull of the sun upon it. Since these two forces of gravitation and movement along an orbit or path are working against each other, and yet never diminishing, one is compelled to agree with the great astronomer, Sir James Jeans, when he says that the more one considers the universe, the more one is compelled to recognise that an Almighty Being started it all, and keeps it going.

So when we consider the immense size of the universe with the countless stars all moving in exact paths, in perfect timing without stopping, we see both God's power and His wisdom. When we think of an atom, unbelievably small, as an orderly arrangement yet filled with tremendous energy, again we are amazed at God's power and wisdom. When we think of the various parts of a cell of a plant or an animal all beautifully made, perfectly arranged and all working harmoniously with each other part, although the cell may be only a hundredth of an inch across, again we have to say, "All thy works shall praise thee, O Lord;" Ps. 145:10.

Furthermore, what most 'scientists' forget when claiming to discuss the origin of the universe is that it is not merely the placing of the sun, moon and stars which is involved, but the very formation, or creation of them in the beginning, and that is entirely beyond man's greatest powers of reason to fathom. This is what no scientist is able or ever will be able to explain. The Bible gives the perfect explanation: "In the beginning God created the heaven and the earth," and in Hebrews 11:3 we read, "Through faith we understand that the worlds were framed by the word of God so that things which are seen were not made of things which do appear," and in Psalm 33 verse 6 we read, "By the word of the Lord were the heavens made, and all the host of them by the breath of his mouth." This was all completed before science even began or man was formed. But seeing there is not one shred of true evidence for the pretended tremendous age of the earth it is significant that the appearance of the rocks, both igneous and sedimentary, agrees with the implied teaching of the Bible that there was volcanic action, with up-lifting of the sea-bed in the first part of the Flood, and it seems there was much lowering of it towards the end of the Flood, when the fountains of the great deep were stopped; see also Psalm 104: 8 & 9.

It has long been taught, since Lyell stated his theory of Uniformity, that the sea-bed has been quiet and undisturbed for many millions of years, although it beats the imagination that anyone could believe this. It is now, however, quite clear that this is not the case. It had been thought that the deepest parts of the ocean-floor were covered with a deep-water type of deposit of considerable thickness which had slowly settled through vast ages; but when borings of several parts of the sea-bed were made, it was found that the deep-water deposit was very thin, and was lying on top of layers of shallow-water deposits. So the sea in many places must have been shallow not so very long ago, a few thousand years perhaps, but not several millions and it must have sunk since.

In addition, Dr. K. K. Landes, Chairman of the Department of Geology at the University of Michigan, writes, "Can we, as seekers after truth, shut our eyes any longer to the obvious fact that large areas of the sea-floor have sunk vertical distances measured in miles?" (Illogical Geology).

These recent findings agree well with the implied teaching of the Flood account mentioned above.

It was after the gradual sinking of the waters that the tops (or heads) of the mountains were seen. Now several modern geologists believe that the mountains show evidence of considerable uplifting during the most recent period of geological activity, which of course was the later part of the Flood period. And hundreds of volcanic mounts in the oceans prove that there has been vast volcanic activity on the sea-bed. All these facts, taken together fit exactly into the pattern of the Flood account without the need of any of the ridiculous adjustments required to try to make them fit, often incongruously, into the vast age theories, where they do not fit anyway.

7

THE MAIN FACTS

We now put together the main facts which we have considered.

We have seen how the oldest nations on earth have accounts of a world-wide Flood in their histories and traditions, which state that one family of people, and two animals of every sort were saved in an Ark. This fact alone speaks volumes.

We know that vast areas of the earth, in fact three quarters of its surface, are covered with water-laid rocks of various depths and composition, which nothing but a world-wide flood could have left. There are vast shoals of fossilised fish in many places, miles in extent, in which the fish clearly died violent deaths and were buried immediately, in some cases before the colour of the scales changed. The waters which did this must have been thrown across the continents by submarine earthquakes of considerable size, while the waters themselves must have contained rock material which would fossilise the fish quickly.

Beds of fossils of almost all types of animals known today are found in all continents, always in distinct species without a single connecting link between any of them, so there is no evidence of evolution, and many evolutionists have had to admit it. A famous one, Sir Arthur Keith, said, "Evolution is unproved and unprovable." He also admitted that the Castenodolo skeletons shattered all the evolutionists' accepted beliefs in the evolution of man.

A salt sea 12,500 feet up in a fold of the Andes mountains could only have been left when the seas covered the highest mountains. In many other parts of the earth there is abundant evidence that vast lakes or seas of salt-water (also left by the Flood) existed in earlier times, e.g. 1280 A.D. when Marco Polo mapped several, but they have dried up, until today only the salt basins are left.

The numerous caves, on high ground in all continents, crammed with the bones of a motley crowd of animals show how these animals fled to these caves from the rising waters.

Dinosaur footprints and large human footprints found together in the fossilised bed of the Paluxy river show that these huge animals instead of dying out millions of years ago, were living on the earth with men. Huge Dinosaur graveyards, Mammoth graveyards and those of horses and other animals show them to have been drowned, and buried in water-laid diluvium.

Fossils of reptiles, amphibians, and invertebrates cannot indicate long periods when the earth was filled with one or the other of these kinds of animals, as claimed by evolutionists, for if they had spent millions of years in peaceful development they would have left no fossils anyway since fossils only form quickly, under sudden burial. Nearly all fossils show violent deaths, mangled remains, and quick burial. Nothing but the effects of a world-wide flood could have left these innumerable fossils, and sedimentary deposits of varying thicknesses from a few inches to many thousands of feet.

As no ape-man has ever been discovered, but the human remains in the lowest deposits are similar to people of today, while many of them are finer specimens than we are, this agrees exactly with the Bible account.